ROARING ROCKETS

For Danny Spiegelhalter and Virgil Tracy—T.M.

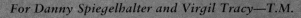KINGFISHER

First Published 1997 by Kingfisher
This edition published 2020 by Kingfisher
an imprint of Macmillan Children's Books
The Smithson, 6 Briset Street, London, EC1M 5NR
Associated companies throughout the world
www.panmacmillan.com

ISBN: 978-1-4472-1267-6

Text copyright © Tony Mitton 1997, 2020
Illustrations copyright © Ant Parker 1997, 2020
Cover design by Peter Clayman

9 8 7 6 5 4 3 2 1

A CIP catalogue record for this book is available from the British Library.

Printed in China

ROARING
ROCKETS

Tony Mitton and Ant Parker

KINGFISHER

Rockets have power. They rise and roar.

This rocket's waiting, ready to soar.

Rockets carry astronauts with cool, white suits,

oxygen helmets and moon boots.

The countdown is finishing: 3, 2, 1 . . .

Action! Blast off! The journey's begun.

Rockets have fuel in great big tanks.

When they're empty, they drop away ... thanks!

Up in space you're really light,

so astronauts strap themselves in tight.

Rockets explore. Through space they zoom,

reaching as far as the big, round moon.

Out comes the lander with legs out ready

and fiery boosters to hold it steady.

Rockets take astronauts out to a place

that's strange and wonderful: silent space . . .

Moon mission over, the lander's left outside.

We're back in the rocket for the long return ride.

Rockets re-enter in a fiery flash
to land at sea with a sizzling splash!

The helicopter carries the brave crew away.
Let's give them a cheer. Hip, hip, hooray!

Rocket parts

moon boots

astronauts need to wear
special protective clothing
when they're walking
on the moon

lunar lander

this takes astronauts
down from the rocket
to land on the moon

oxygen helmet

we need to breathe
oxygen but there is none
in space, so astronauts
carry their own supply which
flows into their helmets

fuel tanks

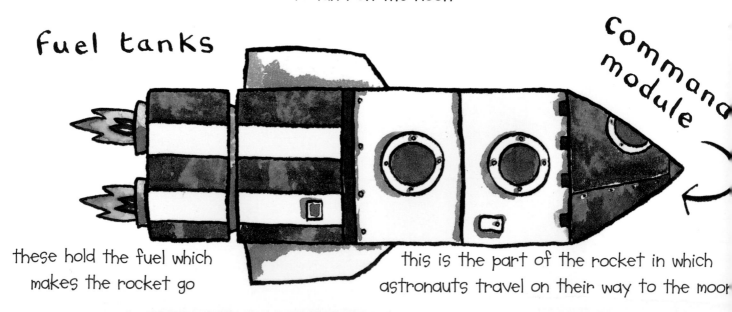

these hold the fuel which
makes the rocket go

command module

this is the part of the rocket in which
astronauts travel on their way to the moon